MASTER YOUR ENGLISH

Common Mistakes

G. C. Davies, L.C.P.
S. M. Dillon
C. Egerton-Chesney
Illustrated by G. C. Davies

D0774091

Basil Blackwell Publisher

To children using this book

You will probably recognize some of the mistakes in this book. You will also probably realise that this book does not deal with every mistake in English that can be made! If you make a mistake, repeatedly, which is not in this book, then don't be a Wilfred — ask your teacher to explain what you are doing wrong.

To teachers using this book

The spelling errors selected for attention are those most commonly encountered by the authors during their combined teaching experience, which covers all ages from five to sixteen.

First published 1981 by
Basil Blackwell Publisher

Reprinted 1982

Phototypeset by Getset (BTS) Ltd, Eynsham, Oxford, in 10/12pt Korinna Regular

Printed in Great Britain at the Camelot Press Ltd, Southampton

CONTENTS

MASTER
YOUR
ENGLISH

I COMMON MISTAKES IN GRAMMAR

1. Verbs in the past tense

Mr Beak is unfortunate enough to be Wilfred's teacher. Wilfred returned to school after being absent.

"What was wrong with you?" asked Mr Beak.

"I catched a cold," said Wilfred.

"No, no, no, Wilfred," said Mr Beak, "I *caught* a cold, I *caught* a cold."

"Oh, hard luck, Sir," piped Wilfred, "Are you better now?"

Wilfred speaks and writes very badly. One of the many mistakes that he makes is to use *verbs in the past tense* wrongly.

He says and writes things like this:

I done the wrong sums. (meaning: I *did* the wrong sums.)

I throwed the box away. (meaning: I *threw* the box away.)

The newspaper come early today. (meaning: the newspaper *came* early today.)

I was froze stiff at the bus stop. (meaning: I was *frozen* stiff at the bus stop.)

Mr. Beak rung the bell. (meaning: Mr Beak *rang* the bell.)

Wallace was stood by the wall. (meaning: Wallace *was standing* by the wall.)

Replace the incorrect verbs by the correct verbs from the box below.

1. Mr Beak asked, "Who drawed the picture?"

2. The window was broke this morning.

3. The helicopter flied over the castle.

4. The sun rised in the east.

5. The pond was completely froze over.

6. When she saw the mess, Sue begun to cry.

7. All my money has been stole!

8. The storm blowed off the roof.

9. It seems a long time since I were ill.

10. I was sat on the old rocking-chair.

11. Nobody has ever rode the old black horse.

12. I seed Tim climbing a tree.

stolen	flew	was	saw
began	sitting	blew	broken
frozen	drew	rose	ridden

2. Singular or plural verb?

Mr Beak growled at Wilfred, "Where were you on Friday, boy?"

Wilfred replied, "I were at the fair, Sir."

"No, no, no, Wilfred," corrected Mr Beak, "I *was* at the fair, I *was* at the fair."

"Oh, was you?" beamed Wilfred, "Great, wasn't it?"

'After Mr Beak's temper had cooled, he tried to explain to his pupil:

Use singular verbs after singular nouns.

Like this: Wilfred is a silly boy.

Mr. Beak goes to church.

The girl went on the beach.

Use plural verbs after plural nouns.

Like this: The boys are clever.

The teachers talk loudly.

Flags fly in the street.

Singular verbs must follow these:

each of   one of   neither of   each

every   none of   nobody either   neither

Examples: Each of the plates *was* broken.

None of the boys *has* brought his kit.

Every one of the players *is* trying.

Complete each sentence by choosing the correct verb from the brackets.

1. Each one of the girls (wears/wear) a clean dress daily.

2. None of the sailors (was/were) leaving the sinking ship.

3. Either the wife or the husband (goes/go) to work.

4. Neither of these shirts (is/are) mine.

5. Each child (looks/look) after its own money.

6. One of the players (has/have) been sent off.

7. Neither Bill nor Ben (belong/belongs) to the badminton club.

8. We (was/were) just walking along the road.

9. Every one of these books (is/are) dirty.

10. None of these children (is/are) to blame.

11. Nobody (is/are) allowed to go home.

12. We (was/were) copying from the book.

3. Pronouns and adjectives

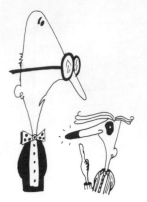

"What happened to you, Wilfred?" asked Mr Beak.

"Len Spong hit I," whined Wilfred, "Him doesn't like I, him doesn't."

"No, no, no, Wilfred," protested Mr Beak, "He doesn't like *me*, he doesn't like *me*."

"Oh' doesn't him, Sir," said Wilfred happily, "then mind him doesn't hit you, then. Or us'll both have black eyes."

Mr Beak explained to Wilfred:

It is incorrect to say: He doesn't like I.

I is the incorrect *pronoun* to use.

It is also incorrect to say: Him doesn't like me.

Him is the incorrect pronoun to use.

It is also incorrect to say: He doesn't like he/she/we/they.

We should say: He doesn't like *him/her/us/them*, and he doesn't like *me*.

Some problems

I or me?

Wilfred and I ate the sweets.

This sentence means:

Wilfred ate the sweets and *I* ate the sweets.

It would sound silly to say: Me ate the sweets.

So we do not say: Wilfred and me ate the sweets.

he or him?
>Len and *he* had a fight.
>Give the money to *him*.

she or her?
>Mary and *she* collected
>ten pounds.
>Why not ask *her*?

them, these or those?
>*These* apples are not ripe.
>Give me *those* chocolates.

>Show *them* how to do it.

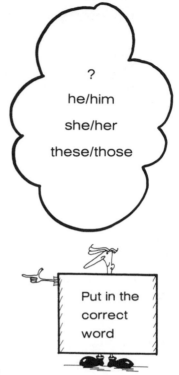

?
he/him
she/her
these/those

Put in the correct word

1. That play bored (I/me) stiff.

2. We think that Mr Beak is always grumbling at (we/us).

3. I said, "Mr Beak is always grumbling at (me/I)."

4. Buy me some of (them/those) peaches, please.

5. Wilfred said that the ball belonged to (him/he) and to no one else.

6. (Those/them) answers are all wrong.

7. Peter said that Sam and (he/him) had been playing together.

8. The dog ran between (I/me) and the gatepost.

9. Between you and (me/I) I think that Wendy will fail her test.

10. Thomas and (I/me) are going to see the next Cup Final.

4. Comparison of adjectives

Wilfred squeaked, "Sir, Wallace Weezle says that I'm the fastest of us two in running. Do you think so?"

"No, no, no, Wilfred," corrected Mr Beak, "I'm the *faster* of us two, I'm the *faster* of us two."

Wilfred thought for a moment.

"Aren't you a bit old to be running, Sir?" he said.

When we compare two things, the adjective usually ends in *-er*.

When we compare more than two things, the adjective usually ends in *-est*.

It is incorrect to say: I am the *fastest* of the two boys.

It is correct to say: I am the *faster* of the two boys.

Mary is the *taller* of the two girls.
He made the *quicker* of the two replies.

Correct these sentences.

1. The best team of the two won the football match.

2. Of the Smith twins, I like Kim the best.

3. Who is fattest, Robert or Philip?

4. Terry is the kindest of the two brothers.

5. Emily is the sweeter of the triplets.

6. Joy has the more brains of the three in the family.

5. Double negatives

"Are you coming on the school trip, Wilfred?" asked Mr Beak.

"No," said Wilfred, sadly, "I haven't got no money."

Mr Beak shook his head.

"No, no, no, Wilfred," he said, "I *have no* money or I *haven't any* money."

"Aw," said Wilfred sympathetically, "Poor old Sir. Aren't you going on the school trip either, then?"

Wilfred has used two negatives in one sentence – have not (*haven't*) and *no*.

We call this a double negative.

If you think about it, a double negative *reverses* the meaning of a sentence.

Correct these sentences.

1. When he got to the shop, Robert could not buy nothing.

2. Wilfred does not learn nothing.

3. Mum could not get no coffee today.

4. Wallace will not try nothing new.

5. The boys weren't going nowhere special.

6. I couldn't see nothing at all.

7. Peter hasn't got no football boots.

8. Wilfred isn't no genius but he isn't no fool either.

6. Confused sentences

In this sentence:

> Henry was sitting on a horse eating a lollipop

. . . was the horse eating a lollipop? . . . or Henry?
We can make the sentence clear by moving a phrase and
putting in commas.

> Henry, sucking a lollipop, was sitting on
> a horse.

Or we can just put in one comma. . .

> Henry was sitting on a horse, eating a
> lollipop.

Or add some words . . . .

> Henry was sitting on a horse *and was*
> eating a lollipop.

Here is another example:

> The stool was sold to a man with carved legs.

Did the man have carved legs? Or the stool? It makes more
sense written like this:

> The stool with carved legs was sold to a man.

Change these sentences to make the meaning clear.

1. Simon was washing the dog in his best clothes.

2. The dog was put to sleep by the vet with a broken leg.

3. The little boy watched the elephant thoughtfully sucking his thumb.

4. Jeremy was hit by a car running across the road.

5. Mrs. Jones bought a doll for a little girl in a plastic bag.

The word "only"

These sentences have the same words but different meanings:

1. *Only* Ron watched United last week.
   (meaning: Ron was the one and only spectator)

2. Ron watched United *only* last week.
   (meaning: Ron watched United as recently as last week)

3. Ron watched *only* United last week.
   (meaning: Ron watched United and no other team)

The position of the word *only* affects the whole meaning of the sentence.

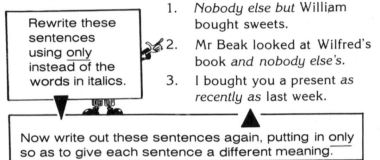

Rewrite these sentences using <u>only</u> instead of the words in italics.

1. *Nobody else but* William bought sweets.

2. Mr Beak looked at Wilfred's book *and nobody else's.*

3. I bought you a present *as recently as* last week.

Now write out these sentences again, putting in only so as to give each sentence a different meaning.

'To' and its verb

To should stand next to its verb when it is used like this:
    to run: to cry: to creep: to wash: to lift

To should not be separated from its verb by an adverb.
We should say: *to go boldly*, not to boldly go
        to limp badly, not to badly limp

Correct these sentences

1. We like to quietly leave.
2. Sue wants to quickly go and catch her bus.
3. The hunter began to noisily blow his horn.

13

II MISTAKES IN USING WORDS

1. A verb or a noun?

These words can be spelt

As a *verb* with an **s**		as a *noun* with a **c**	
practise	license	practice	licence
advise	prophesy	advice	prophecy

Like this:

> I prophesy that Mr. Pringle will advise you to buy a TV licence and you should follow his advice − it is much better to practise honesty.

Write out these sentences, choosing the correct word from the brackets.

1. The old sailor made a (*prophecy/prophesy*) that the high tide would bring danger.

2. A dog (*licence/license*) only costs a little.

3. You should (*practice/practise*) your guitar every day.

4. I would (*advise/advice*) you to listen.

5. Take my (*advise/advice*) and never (*prophecy/prophesy*) what the weather will be.

2. Overworked words

We tend to overwork some words, especially:

> nice   said   got.

Read this mini-story:

> "What a nice surprise!" said the old lady. "You have got all those logs for me. How very nice of you. Now look at what I got in the baker's today − a nice cream cake."
>
> "Oh, how nice," said Tim, trying to hide his disappointment. He would have preferred a bag of nice crisps.

Now read this part of the story on page 14, in which the overworked words have been changed into more interesting ones. Finish the rest of the story in the same way.

> "What a lovely surprise!" cried the old lady. "You have chopped all those logs for me. How very kind of you."

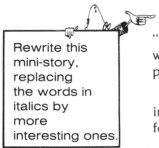

Rewrite this mini-story, replacing the words in italics by more interesting ones.

"Hurry up!" *said* Tim excitedly, waving a parcel wrapped in *nice* paper.

"I can't hurry," *said* Kim impatiently, "I'm making myself *nice* for Henry's party."

"You couldn't look *nice*, whatever you did," *said* Tim.

Kim turned pink. 'Try being *nice* like Henry for a change," she *said* furiously.

"Huh," *said* Tim, making a face, "It's all right for him, living in that *nice* house with that *nice* swimming pool. And he's got that *nice* car and that *nice* dog, too."

"You're jealous!" *said* Kim.

"Nonsense," *said* Tim. "It's just that I wish we hadn't *got* him such a *nice* present. In fact I think I'll throw it away."

He pretended to throw the parcel out of the open window. Unfortunately, the parcel flew from his hand, shot through the window and landed with a crash on the ground below the window.

3. Needless repetition

Small Vik and Very Small Vik rushed into the Great Vikhall.

"We've seen a Fat Poggie!" gasped Small Vik.

"A Fat Poggie!" echoed Very Small Vik.

"In the Dark Woods!" puffed Small Vik.

"Dark Woods!" repeated Very Small Vik.

"The first for years and years!" gabbled Small Vik.

"Years and Years!" chattered Very Small Vik.

Small Vik turned to Very Small Vik.

"Why are you repeating everything I say?" he snapped, "You sound like an echo."

Very Small Vik looked hurt and his whiskers drooped sadly.

Very Small Vik was over-doing things, as usual.

He was repeating phrases when it was not necessary.

Examples: a forest of trees
a quick-firing machine gun
a three-wheeled tricycle
a hundred-year-old centenarian

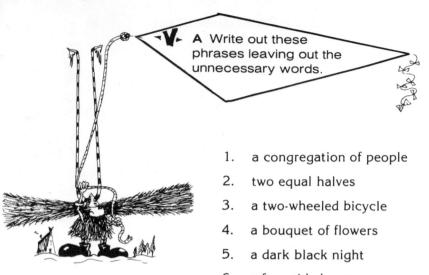

A Write out these phrases leaving out the unnecessary words.

1. a congregation of people
2. two equal halves
3. a two-wheeled bicycle
4. a bouquet of flowers
5. a dark black night
6. a four-sided square
7. a solid-fuel coal stove
8. a nasal infection of the nose.

B Rewrite these sentences, leaving out the unnecessary words.

1. The design is inside a five-sided pentagon.
2. All the team's supporters are united together.
3. That's a neat circular round hole!
4. Divide the cake into four quarters.
5. Lower the injured man down carefully.
6. You should be there by 2 p.m. this afternoon.
7. The poor dog was fatally killed.
8. This toothache in my mouth is dreadful and it's driving me madly insane.

4. Using the wrong words

Private Bonehead does everything wrong. Sergeant Snap grumbled at him so much during drill-parade that poor Bonehead asked Private Pop, "Please *learn* me how to march properly."

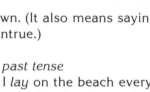

"No, no," said Pop, trying not to laugh, "I'll *teach* and you will *learn*."

Words such as *teach* and *learn* are often confused and used wrongly.
So are these words: **lie** and **lay**.
To lie means the act of lying down. (It also means saying something which you know is untrue.)
Examples:

present tense	*past tense*
I *lie* on the beach every day.	I *lay* on the beach every day.
Grandma *lies* down after tea.	Grandma *lay* down after tea.

To lay means to spread something out.
Examples:

present tense	*past tense*
She lays the table.	She *laid* the table.
He lays the carpet in the other room.	He *laid* the carpet in the other room.

It is wrong to use *lay* like this:
Lay down and go to sleep.

I was laying on the grass.

Bonehead is laying down, fast asleep.

Bonehead is *lying* down, not laying down!

lend and **borrow**
>We lend *to* and borrow *from*

More words
that are
confused

beat and **win**
>We beat *someone else* (in a race).
>We win *a prize*.

(*beat* can also mean to hit someone)

hanged and **hung**
>*People* are *hanged* (put to death.)
>*Things* are *hung* (pictures, clothes, poultry, etc.)

Correct
these
sentences.

1. James won Lisa at 'Scrabble'.

2. Can I lend tenpence to buy a comic, please, Mum?

3. I know my coat was hanged on the first hook.

4. You had better go and lay on the bed.

5. Go and ask Mr. Smith if you can lend his garden fork.

6. Will you learn me how to do Judo?

7. Dick Turpin was hung at Tyburn.

8. Lie those fragile ornaments carefully on the cottonwool.

9. Captain Crackle was laying on the floor.

10. If you are good, I will learn you how to knit.

19

there and **their**

To do with *people*
        Their drums beat
        Their feet tramp
        Their boots shine
        Their badges glitter
        Their heads are held high
(Think — an *heir* is a *person*)

Some more words often confused

To do with *places*
        March over *there*. Where? *There!*
        Don't put the chairs over *there*.
        Where shall I put them, then?
        Over *there*, right on the opposite side!

its and **it's**

its is a *possessive adjective* — the same kind of word as *his* and *her*
it's (with apostrophe) is short for *it is*

        The dog has eaten all *its* dinner.
        It's no use trying; *it's* too late.

Put the correct words into the spaces.

1. The rabbit rubbed _____ ears.

2. They went abroad on _____ holidays.

3. That building over _____ is our school.

4. _____ no use crying over spilt milk.

5. Snow fell here and _____.

6. However hard they tried, _____ efforts were useless; the load could not be moved over _____.

Still more confusion

These words are often mixed up –

of and **off**

If we *say* them properly we should not confuse them.

Half a pound *of* rice, please.

Robert walked *off* the pitch angrily.

It is incorrect to use the two words, off and of, *together*.

'Thik Vik fell *off of* the wall' is wrong.

It should be: 'Thik Vik fell *off* the wall'.

Put in the correct words
<u>of</u> or <u>off</u>

1. Private Pop marched _____ the parade-ground.

2. The match is _____ because the ground is frozen.

3. Pik Vik had a load _____ wood for the bonfire.

4. Sing me a song _____ days gone by.

5. Top Vik was the first Vik to jump _____ the Longboot on to the beach.

6. Poor old Uncle Sid fell _____ the highest building in the town.

21

Just one more . . . . . .

have and of

This is wrong: I would of told you if you'd asked.

This is right: I would *have* told you if you'd asked.

Do this mini-Beaktest.

Correct these sentences. Some of them contain more than one mistake

1. Ask those boys if there boots are clean.

2. Its no good the dog asking for it's dinner yet.

3. Don't walk of when I am telling you of.

4. Grandad said, "That boy will end up being hung."

5. Its no use you laying on the settee, my lad.

6. Sir, will you learn me how to play badminton?

7. I've told you twice to get off of my wall.

8. There new clothes are hanged over their.

9. I'd like to lend five pence off of you, please.

10. Lie the poor chap down their, then he can lay in comfort.

11. The cat arched it's back and fell off of the chair.

12. It would of been easier to lend the book off of Sally.

5. Words that sound alike

Pik Vik makes all the Ho! swords for the Viks. One day, he held a "Clearance Sale".

Slik Vik saw the notice and collapsed with laughter.

"What a notice," he screamed, "Oh, dear, oh dear. Great leaping Fudge-Scuttles. What a notice!"

"It sounds all right to me," sniffed Pik Vik, in an injured tone. "What's wrong with it?"

Slik Vik explained.

Pik Vik had used words that *sound* like the words he wanted, but the ones he chose have an entirely different meaning.

Find out what words Pik Vik *should* have used.
Unfortunately, a dictionary will not help you a great deal.

Here are some more examples of words that sound alike:

bare	bear
hole	whole
made	maid
flour	flower

23

Words often confused

to	Go *to* bed.
too	Can I come, *too*?
two	*Two* teas, please.

passed	The tortoise *passed* the hare.
past	Small Vik walked *past* the notice.
won	Liverpool *won* the F. A. Cup.
one	Only *one* person may enter.
here	The vicar was *here* yesterday.
hear	Can you *hear* the bells?

Correct these sentences.

1. May I eat too buns?

2. I have been asleep for the passed hour.

3. Is it time two go home?

4. You can have just won drink.

5. Wilfred past me on the way home.

6. Winston is far to tall for that job.

7. I am not deaf – I can here quite clearly.

8. The champion kept the trophy and one a medal.

9. Who past the winning post first?

10. Did you here me? I told you to come hear.

Some more words often confused

no and know
There is *no* need for anyone to *know* our secret.

write/right *Write* the letter in the *right* way.

witch/which In *which* part of the woods does the old *witch* live?

wood/would *Would you be kind enough to pass me a piece of smooth wood?*

piece/peace Give the child another *piece* of cake then we shall have some *peace* and quiet.

Correct these sentences.

1. Wood you like some tea?

2. Is it to be piece or war?

3. It is impossible to read anything that you right in your book.

4. Only I no that answer.

5. In witch box will I find the towels?

6. There is know way out of this maze.

7. You said that you wood share the food with me.

8. First put forward your left foot and then your write foot.

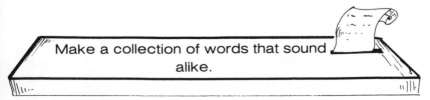

Make a collection of words that sound alike.

III GENERAL SPELLING MISTAKES

1. Spelling "clangers"

During the second World War the Royal
Air Force had its own *slang*.

For example:

Airman Erk

"bang on" meant "exactly right"

"to drop a clanger" meant "to make
a bad mistake".

Most children drop *spelling* clangers
sometimes. (So do a lot of adults!)

Help Airman Erk, the 'clanger collector' to collect the
spelling clangers in the sentences below. Write out the
sentences correctly when you have found all the mistakes.

To make it a little easier, the clangers are in *italics*.

1. I *hop* you are feeling *beter*.
2. Sally *toled* me to go away.
3. Your *ansers* are all *rong*.
4. Tea is being served in the *dinning* room.
5. The *docter siad*, "Take these tablets."
6. If Mandy *gose*, can I go *to*?
7. What a *pritty babby*!
8. Your *handrighting* is *awfull*.
9. Wear your *sandles* in the *libary*.
10. Santa *triped* and fell down the *chimley*.

2. Eight spelling rules

Here are eight spelling rules that can help you to avoid dropping clangers. Remember there are *exceptions* to most spelling rules.

1 *i* goes before *e* (where the vowel sound is *ee*) except after *c*.

   brief   priest   receive

Some exceptions: *weigh   their   sleigh* (Here the vowel sound is *ay*)

2 When you add *-ing, -ed, -est, -ies* (and other vowel *suffixes*) to words of one syllable after a short vowel, double the last letter.

   stop – *stopped*   hot – *hotter*

Exceptions: words ending in *w x y*
             words with a double vowel or a long vowel
             leap – *leaped*   foul – *fouled*

3 If a word ends in *silent e*, drop the *e* when adding a vowel suffix (*-ing, -ance,* etc.). Do not drop it when adding a consonant suffix (*-ment, -ful,* etc.)

   save – *saving* ⎫
   fame – *famous* ⎬ *e* dropped
   amaze – *amazement* ⎫
   love – *lovely* ⎬ *e* not dropped

4 Learn words with *silent letters*:

   psalm   lamb   through   guess

5 *q* is *always* followed by *u*: *queen quack*

6 Words like *sorrowful, beautiful, fulfil* have *only one l* at the end.

27

7 When you add *-ful* or *-fully* to words ending with *y* after a consonant, change the *y* into *i*.

    pity – *pitiful*   mercy – *mercifully*

8 These expressions are *two words* and not one:

    all right (not 'alright') *thank you* (not 'thankyou')

A Correct these sentences.

1. When will you be leaveing?
2. The frog was hoping along.
3. Grandma was pating the dog.
4. Give Jim a peice of pie.
5. I kept droping off to sleep.
6. That was a qick meal!
7. I shall be alright tomorrow.
8. Plums are plentifull now.
9. He triped on the pavement.
10. What a dutyfull officer Captain Crackle is!

Example: To hit something hard: *knock*

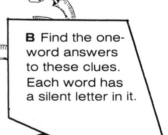

B Find the one-word answers to these clues. Each word has a silent letter in it.

1. A young sheep
2. Unable to speak
3. A king's wife
4. Make a garment with wool and special needles
5. What you do with a pen
6. The _____ of Hearts who stole the tarts
7. Branch of a tree
8. Most people have four fingers and one _____ on each hand

3. The troublesome apostrophe

Hand in all
boot's and
shirt's today

"You've dropped two clangers for me to pick up," moaned Airman Erk.

"Where? What?" asked Corporal Fiddle, who is in charge of the uniform stores.

Erk pointed out the mistakes on the notice that Fiddle was about to put on the door of the stores.

The (') is an *apostrophe* (say app-oss-troff-ee). It shows either

1 That a letter or letters have been left out.

Example: *don't = do not*
o'clock = of the clock
I'm = I am

or

2 Possession — it tells you who owns something.

Erk's bucket
Fiddle's notice

Plurals are *not* made by using apostrophes.
Not boot's but *boots*   Not shirt's but *shirts*

Write down
the plurals of
these nouns

1. bucket	7. box
2. biscuit	8. potato
3. blanket	9. flower
4. hat	10. orange
5. tomato	11. crisp
6. record	12. lady.

29

Correct these sentences. The mistakes in sentences 1 to 8 are in italics. In sentences 9 to 15 they are not.

1. The water was *driping* on the floor.

2. I am *hopping* to go to Wimbledon next year.

3. These *spot's* are *painfull*.

4. *Witch* box of *Johns* apples shall I *wiegh*?

5. Will it be *alright* if Mark says "*thankyou*" for his present later?

6. Uncle *siad* that his corgi *pupies* are very *playfull*.

7. Laura *sliped* in the deep *sno* and had to *lay their* for some *minuets*.

8. The programme *stared* Elvis *keynotes* band of *musicans*.

9. Both team's were heaveing on the rope's.

10. Its to bad, both piano's are out of tune.

11. Shall we eat are sangwidges in the libary or in the dinning-room?

12. Although Wilfreds throat was sore, he tryed to tork quitely.

13. The qeen was quiet reddy to recieve her gests.

14. The dog snarled savagly at the gilty man.

15. The peple could not beleive there eyes.

Do you make mistakes like Wilfred does?
Try Mr Beak's test and see if you do!

1. Choose the right word from the brackets to complete each sentence.

   a) The apple (falled/fell) off the tree.

   b) The coat has never been (worn/wore).

   c) Wilfred (ran/run) across the hall.

2. Choose the right verb to complete these sentences.

   a) None of the children (is/are) allowed to go home.

   b) The man and his dogs (run/runs) across the field.

   c) Everyone (are/is) listening to the speaker.

   d) Mandy, with several others, (was/were) taken to hospital.

3. Choose the right word to complete these sentences correctly.

   a) Pass me some of (them/those) cakes.

   b) John said, "(He/Him) and (I/me) will go."

   c) Sally and (me/I) will help you.

4. Correct these sentences.

   a) The little girl is the happiest of the pair.

   b) Wendy does not know nothing about it.

   c) It is wise to carefully think before you write.

   d) The old soldier was run over by a car wandering across the road.

5. Rewrite these sentences, replacing the words *nice, got,* and *said*, with more interesting words.

   a) Paul got measles and he thought that staying in bed was not very nice.

   b) "What a nice day!" said Peter at the top of his voice.

6. Rewrite these sentences, leaving out the unnecessary words.

   a) We saw a medieval abbey dating back to the Middle Ages.

   b) The gangster received a fatal shot that killed him.

7. Correct these sentences.

   a) My dad learnt me how to fish.

   b) The picture was hanged in the gallery.

   c) A lovely seen was spread before our eyes.

   d) The ball smashed the window-pain.

8. Write down and spell correctly one-word answers to these clues.

   a) A line of people waiting for a bus. (*5 letters*)

   b) Full of beauty. (*9 letters*)

   c) The number before nine (write it as a *word*). (*5 letters*)

   d) Applause, using the hands. (*8 letters*)

   e) Someone who steals. (*5 letters*)